The Legal Nurse Consulting Workbook:
How to Turn Your Nursing Knowledge into a Successful Consulting Practice

By Lorie A. Brown, R.N., M.N., J.D.

The Legal Nurse Consulting Workbook:
How to Turn Your Nursing Knowledge into a
Successful Consulting Practice
©2011 Lorie A. Brown. All rights reserved.
©2012 Lorie A. Brown, All rights reserved.

Copyright Information

Table of Contents:

Introduction

We are about to embark on an amazing journey together—one which will result in you having a successful legal nurse consulting business. So first, let me tell you about myself and why I chose to write this book.

In 1982, I graduated from nursing school with a BSN from Indiana University. I knew I wanted to continue my education, so I headed west, moved to California and received a MN from UCLA in 1984. My Masters was in nursing administration and clinical nurse specialist in medical surgical nursing. I thought about obtaining a doctorate in nursing but did not want to teach.

I then went through a midlife crisis—early, I guess. I got divorced and went to law school, graduating in 1990. I knew I wanted to combine my nursing with law and became a medical malpractice defense attorney. At the firm where I worked, I defended hospitals, nurses and physicians throughout the state of Indiana.

One of my jobs was to develop new business. I hated it. I thought to successfully market one's business, it was important to find out what the clients like to establish a relationship. It seemed that all the claims adjusters for insurance companies liked to play golf, drink and smoke cigars—not necessarily in that order. Since I was not a golfer, smoker or drinker (sounds like a '70s song), I was lost. I could not get new business for the life of me.

One day, one of the female associates at the firm was in a golf outing with some prospective clients, and I actually saw her with a cigar in her mouth. I was not willing to stoop to that level to get business.

Needless to say, I dreaded marketing and was lousy at it. So what happened for me to become a successful marketer and be able to share my information with you?

I loved my job and did a great job (except for marketing) until the bomb dropped. The insurance company which was the major source of my practice went out of business. I thought my partners would stand by me. After all, partners stick together, right? Wrong, I found myself without a job, pregnant with my second child, a huge mortgage and car payment, and the sole source of support for my family. (Do you have any idea how expensive health insurance is, especially when you are pregnant?)

Now, no one was going to hire me because I did not have clients to bring to another firm and was pregnant. (That's evidently a sin for a female attorney: Thou shall not reproduce as it reduces your billable hours!)

After spending days crying on my kitchen floor and vomiting due to morning sickness, I woke up one morning and it hit me: "If it is meant to be, it is up to me." I could not go back to a firm and did not want to travel and be in court as I had been. I wanted to raise my family and be home for my children.

So I read all the marketing books I could get my hands on and hired a business coach. I realized that to have a successful business, you not only need the knowledge, but the proper mindset. I committed myself to developing a successful medical legal consulting practice. In 1999, Brown Law Office and my second son were born. And today, more than a decade later, I have several legal nurse consultants with various specialties working for me, and I have a nationwide presence and make more money than I did as a partner in a law firm.

You're probably thinking: "Well, you are an attorney so it was easy for you." This could not be further from the truth. I had numerous obstacles to overcome—even more than most legal nurse consultants.

The first hurdle was that I was a defense attorney, so I had to show the plaintiff attorneys that I could be trusted. Next, several legal nurse consultants where I live charged a whole lot less money than I did. How do I know this? I used them when I did defense work.

But I did overcome those obstacles, and I am extremely grateful to my business development coach for giving me the tools to grow my consulting practice. This book is a labor of love (seems fitting, as I was pregnant when all this started) and a way to share my knowledge with other legal nurse consultants. Through my journey, I realized it is more important to collaborate than to compete.

It is my hope that you will read this book, implement the tools I have provided, and gain the mindset of success. We were all meant to succeed. It is my hope that I will have inspired you to develop a successful consulting business with all the joys and freedom that come with it.

Remember: If it is meant to be, it is now up to you. So now let's get down to how to succeed.

Happy Marketing,

Lorie

Notes

Chapter One:

The Mindset of Success

We all have dreams of having a successful business. We may want to quit our day job. We want financial independence. Those of us who become legal nurse consultants (LNC) do so often because we want control over our hours, schedules and work environments. We don't want to be a prisoner of the hospital and have to work weekends and holidays.

So why is mindset so important? Think about when you worked on a highly effective nursing unit (yes they do exist!). What are the attributes that made it effective? Here are a few to consider:

- Teamwork
- Commitment—doing whatever it takes to help the patient
- Communication
- Trust
- Hard work
- Compassion for patients
- Responsibility (to self, team and patient)

- Contribution—doing what is wanted and needed by the team

The list can go on and on. Of those attributes, which ones are skills that must be learned, and which ones are a mindset, or both? All of these are mindset or both. Therefore, skill has very little to do with it. *That* is why a mindset of success is so important. *Taking Action*

Consider this formula:

Goals/Dreams + *Study/Action* = *Results, reality*

Intention + Action = Results

Intention is something you've already decided about your future. It was your intention to be a nurse. You were not going to let anything get in the way. No matter how you got there, you all achieved the results, you all became RNs. Or LPNs.

Now you want to become a legal nurse consultant. Did you let anything stop you in learning how to be an LNC? I doubt it, or you would not be reading this book. In fact, some of you had to come up with thousands of dollars just to attend the course to become an LNC. This same intention is critical for you to succeed as an LNC.

This is not wishing. Wishing is not going to produce the results you want. You must take action.

Action is what you decide to do next, or the direction you decide to take to get your results.

Results, of course, come from your intention and your action. How much of the formula is intention and how much is action? In my experience, intention makes up 99% of your results. There are endless ways (or actions) to get to the same result. But you must intend it with all your heart, to your core, for you to achieve the results that you want.

You must also be willing to not let circumstances get in the way of your success. If it's your intention to be a successful LNC, you will make it happen. There's no back door. Quitting is not an option. If your intention is to have a successful business, you'll make it happen. You will take the actions that produce the results that you want. Some people are so afraid of failure that they never begin or even set themselves up to fail. With intention, failure is not an option.

Look at Olympic athletes. I am reminded of the Summer Olympics in Atlanta where gymnast Kerri Strug ran on a broken ankle to vault over a horse and lead the American team to a gold medal in the all around competition. Her intention was so strong that failure was not an option.

If you are truly intentional about your business and take the appropriate action, there is no other result but success. But to be successful, it requires you to get out of your comfort zone and do things that are out of the box.

It was not comfortable for Kerri Strug to run on a broken ankle, but look at the result. This process is called stretching. If you talk to any successful person, they will tell you that the journey to success was not easy, that you must stretch, think out of the box and get out of your comfort zone to overcome a lot of obstacles.

For nurses, this is particularly true. We are caregivers, not business people. It is true that because of our training and personalities, we are gifted at understanding and meeting a patient's needs. If you think of your client as a "patient" whose needs you are trying to understand and meet, this is a logical transition. To be a successful legal nurse consultant, though, we need to learn the necessary business skills, including marketing.

We had the mindset to be a successful nurse, but now need to shift that mindset to become a successful business person. As a nurse, when we were hired by an employer, we did not need to worry about how to get business, how to bill and how to manage the finances. We knew how to do our jobs, and we were good at it. As a successful LNC, you may know how to review a case, write a great report and prepare an excellent chronology, but you may not have the mindset or skills to be successful in business.

So fasten your seatbelt because, like on an airplane, the take-off is a little bumpy as you go through the clouds (obstacles). Once you reach cruising altitude, it is smooth flying. Now it is time to get out of your comfort zone and take off.

Visualize Your Destination

With that said, most of us need a roadmap before we take off. Stop and meditate. Yes, I said "meditate." This may be out of the comfort zone for some of you, but it is important.

Shortly I'm going to ask you to project yourself into the future. For five to 10 minutes, visualize what your life is going to be like when you have your successful practice: what it's going to *look* like, what it's going to *smell* like, what it's going to *taste* like, how many cases you're going to have.

It is important for you to really feel what being successful will be like for you. The emotion must be there for your passion and desire of a successful business to become a reality. This is your destination.

To reach this destination, you will need a variety of things. The first is marketing—that is, you will need to understand your market and promote your business. We'll talk more about that later. But first, you need to imagine your destination.

Exercise: *Document your experience visualizing where you would like your business to be in one year from now. Be specific including number of clients, number of cases, income generated and the feelings that accompany your success.*

One year from now I will

Be a successful
LNC with my own office in Fla.
with enough cases to
provide $100K of income, minimum
I feel like a total
success, happy,
confident, fulfilled
professionally and
be at peace with
finances

I ~~am~~ will also begin
working on my pt. advocate
business with a few clients
integrating my LNC business.
I will figure this out.

As you begin building your legal nurse consulting business, you will need to continually visualize your success. Do it often. You are training your mind to overcome any doubts or hesitancies you have about succeeding, and making that success seem inevitable.

I also suggest you write a goal card. A goal card is a visual reminder of the results you want to produce. It should be stated in present tense with a date of accomplishment and express gratitude for the results.

My goal card in writing this book was dated August 12, 2009 (so I was a little off on timing!). Here's what I wrote:

"I am so happy and grateful now that I finished my LNC marketing ebook and have shared it with thousands of LNCs across the country and they now know they have everything they need to have a successful consulting business. The ebook has sold 1,000 copies, and several LNCs have told me how much their business has increased as a result of this book. It warms my heart to know I have helped so many people have a successful business."

Yes, I was late in getting this book finished. No, actually I just picked the wrong date! But it was my intention to finish and now it's done. See how important mindset is!

Once you write your goal card, I suggest you carry it with you in your purse, pocket or wallet every day. Read it twice a day. The best time to read it is when you first wake up and right before you go to sleep. Remember, keeping it in your wallet and reading it alone will not produce the results you want—**you need to take action.**

Exercise: *Prepare your goal card.*

[date] I am so happy and grateful now that

I have started my LNC and PA study.
I ~~also~~ will be working in the LNC
field very soon - by Oct.- Nov. and complete
study in e.a. by Dec. 2021.
By end of year 2022 I will have a
successful business with enough clients
to give very comfortably and help others
at the same time!

It is also important to review your results. In writing this book, I had to ask myself what got in the way of me getting it done when I said I would. This needs to be done from a place of love rather than criticism. I am my worst critic, but criticism did not move me toward my goal; it will not for you either.

Ultimately I had to confront my fears about embracing success and doing something out of the box. I knew I was a successful attorney and legal nurse consultant, but what about an author? I realized that I did not complete the book sooner because if I completed it, no one might buy it and I would have failed. Obviously, this is not true as you are reading it. Once I confronted my fears and moved past them, I was able to complete this book.

What are *your* fears of being successful? Do you feel you do not deserve it? Do you feel you are uncomfortable with attorneys? You need to confront whatever is stopping you and move past it. (This is where a good business coach is invaluable.)

Let me address the uncomfortable-with-attorneys fear. First of all, attorneys can smell fear a mile away. If they sense you are uncomfortable, they are not going to trust you with their client's confidential medical information. But you can overcome this fear.

Remember when you first became a nurse and were intimidated by the physicians? But now, you basically tell the physicians what to do and what orders you want. The same is true of attorneys. You have a specialized knowledge and information that they don't have, or they would not hire you. Attorneys put on their pants one leg at a time just like you, me and the physicians.

This also goes back to mindset. Will a mindset of discomfort with attorneys help you build a successful business? No. If you want to be successful, you must overcome your discomfort with attorneys. You may want to place yourself in situations like a seminar where you need to interact with a lot of attorneys.

Yes, I know this sounds uncomfortable, but what did I tell you? You have to get out of your comfort zone to be successful. Just as with the doctors, it really does get easier with time.

You probably have heard the phrase "fake it until you make it." With the mindset of success and your continued reading of the goal card, you will soon

 think, feel and act as if you are already successful. The cases are on their way even though they are not on your desk yet. You will appear to attorneys as confident and successful so they will want to work with you.

Exercise: *If you have been at this for a while, think back to a year ago. Write down the results you produced. Looking back, how successful was your business? Did you accomplish what you wanted? If not, why not? What got in your way? What needs to be different this year?*

[Date] In a year I

_____

_____

_____

_____

_____

_____

_____

_____

_____

_____

_____

_____

_____

_____

Exercise: *If you are new to the LNC world (or not!), write down what your fears are, what obstacles you need to overcome and then rephrase the fears and obstacles into a positive more empowering statement. For example, if you write "I am afraid of failure," rephrase it as "I embrace my success." If you write "I don't have time to market my consulting practice because of my work at the hospital," rephrase it as "I have all the time I need to successfully market my practice."*

My fears:

Fear of failure = I embrace Success

Fear of sounding stupid - I sound confident

Not having all the answers

I'll have the answers

I need to give

and sound confident

My obstacles to overcome:

Fear of failure

Fear of not saying the right thing

Lack of confidence

Don't deserve success

Rephrase them as empowering statements:

I embrace success and am successful.

I say the appropriate things with confidence

I'm confident in my own skin and know more than attys about health/medical

I work hard and deserve success. I am as good as anyone else who is successful.

I have prepared my whole life for this- LNC and it is part of who I am.

Notes

Notes

_____

_____

_____

_____

_____

_____

_____

_____

_____

_____

_____

_____

_____

_____

_____

_____

Chapter Two:

Needs-Based Marketing

Marketing is the entire process of getting goods and services into the hands of the consumer. I use what I call "needs-based marketing." Needs-based marketing is based on finding the customer's needs and then communicating to the customer how you can meet those needs. If you feel uncomfortable marketing yourself, think of yourself as a problem solver, not someone selling a service.

For an LNC, that means determining the attorney's needs and then telling him how you can fill those needs or provide solutions. Eighty percent of your marketing should be about the attorneys, their problems and what you can do to help solve those problems. Only 20 percent of your marketing should be about your knowledge, skills and abilities you bring to solving problems.

My experience has been that most legal nurse consultants will say to an attorney, "I'm a legal nurse consultant. I can review your records to determine the standard of care and summarize your records for you to help you determine if there is a case or not."

This is often followed by an inaudible "So what?" reaction from the attorney. As an LNC you'll need to be able to pass that "so what?" test.

Here's another example. If I say to you, "I can paint your house," you're going to say, "I don't need my house painted" or "I live in a brick house." You're essentially telling me *So what?*

However, if you might need your house painted and if I say to you, "I'm going to save you time and money by painting your house this fall before the weather turns bad and those rough spots get any worse during the winter, and I can do it for a reasonable rate," now I've got your attention. I have shown you my value based on your need, my value. And I've said it concisely.

As an LNC, you'll need to figure out what value and benefits you bring to the attorney. And you'll need to be able to say it concisely because that's what's going to get his or her attention. Attorneys are the target of a lot of marketing because of their position in the community. They are busy and don't have time to listen to sales pitches. So they turn on the *salesdar* (like radar), and they avoid sales pitches like the plague.

I will teach you techniques of how to get in the door of potential attorney clients shortly. But first, by recognizing the attorneys needs, you will not come off as a sales person but as someone who can genuinely benefit the attorneys practice.

One way to introduce yourself to an attorney and show your value is through *an elevator drill.*

The Elevator Drill

An elevator drill is basically a 30- to 60-second blurb that you give the attorney. It expresses the value and benefits of what you're going to bring that attorney so he will ask you to tell him more about your services. It's your executive summary. If you can't summarize it on the short elevator ride to his or her office, it's too much information.

The components of an elevator drill are:

a. What you do.

b. What benefits or value you bring. These will be different depending if you are marketing plaintiff attorneys or defense attorneys. Remember the plaintiff attorneys represent the patient or injured party and the defendant attorneys represent the doctors, health care providers or alleged wrong doers.

c. Three ways you can bring that value. (When making your value statement, it's important to know your competition. One easy way to do this: Look at the websites of different legal nurse consultants to find the three main things they say about their services.) *3 main things*

Research competition

d. How you can work together with the attorney. (Using an open-ended question to get the attorney talking about his needs is an excellent approach here.)

My elevator drill goes like this: "Hello, I am Lorie Brown. I am a nurse and an attorney, and I consult with attorneys on medical issues in their cases. I can save you time and money by prescreening your case for merit, researching medical issues and finding the appropriate expert so you have everything you need to be successful with your case. How can my services benefit you?"

You might be thinking, "Lorie, you can't possibly get business from introducing yourself on an elevator." Well, I do.

Once in Fort Wayne, Indiana, I was on an elevator with a gentleman who looked like an attorney. I engaged him in conversation, found out that he was indeed an attorney and gave him my elevator drill. When the elevator stopped on his floor, I stepped out with him and gave him my card. I followed up with a letter.

Now I didn't know the guy from Adam, but thanks to my elevator drill and follow-up he turned into a good client for me. He was primarily a criminal attorney, but he had a personal injury case that he really needed my expertise on the medical injuries.

That shows the importance of timing when you meet someone who could be a client for you. This is a key point to remember: "No" is not rejection; it just means "I don't need your services right now."

So you take the "No" and you ask, "Do you mind if I call you back in a month or so to see what your needs are then?" Asking for permission to follow up is very reassuring to me so I don't feel like a stalker! Make sure you keep a door open that could lead to him or her becoming a client.

Now it's time for you to begin pulling together your own elevator drill.

Exercise: *First fill out these questions:*

What I do:

I'm a LNC, analyze records, research medical issues [prescreen cases for merit] and find appropriate medical experts so your cases can be successful.

_____

_____

_____

_____

What benefits or value I bring:

I can ~~save~~ you time
and money

_____

_____

_____

_____

_____

Three ways I bring this value: I can provide you with:

1. I can assist c̄ plaintiff or defendants understanding of plaintiff and defendant

2. ☆ Extremely familiar c̄ medical records and documentation from IS background

3. ☆ Broad and focused knowledge of procedural, OR, ICUs areas including pharmacy and nursing

How I can work with an attorney:

How can my services benefit you?

_____

_____

_____

_____

_____

Now, condense the information above into a pitch for your business that you can deliver in a minute and a half to two minutes.

_____

_____

_____

_____

_____

_____

_____

_____

_____

_____

_____

_____

_____

_____

_____

_____

_____.

Notes

Notes

Chapter Three:

The "Ask" and Overcoming Objections

Once you've developed and given your "elevator drill" presentation, you have to ask for the business. Always make the "ask."

Remember to approach your business from the standpoint that everybody wants to help people. Others typically want to help you maintain or get your business off the ground, too. So if you just ask for their help, that is, ask for their business, they will be more likely to give you a shot. Approaching your business and your marketing in this way can be really helpful. Business is everywhere; you just have to ask.

An attorney with whom I worked is a perfect example of this strategy. It appeared that business simply dropped at his feet. I was always amazed, so I asked him what his secret was. His response: "People want to help people. You just have to ask for the business." That was the best advice.

We are sometimes so afraid that people are going to say no that we don't want to ask for their business. Don't be afraid—ASK. The worst they can say is "no." And "no" is neutral. It is nothing against you.

A good ask is an open-ended question such as "How can we work together?", combined with sharing details of how you would work with the attorney. I know this is uncomfortable but it is necessary and works.

For example, let's say you meet an attorney and you ask, "How can we work together?"

She says, "I have a client coming in next week. She had a botched gall bladder surgery. Can you help me?"

You reply, "Certainly. If we work together, I'd like you to send me the records. I'll prepare a timeline of events called a chronology, give you relevant research and refer you to an expert."

"This is just what I need!" the attorney says, and you're in business.

Exercise: *Imagine you have just given your elevator drill to an attorney. He says, "I have a client who was given the wrong medication during an operation. Can you help me?" You say:*

"
_____

_____

_____

_____

_____

_____

_____

_____

"
_____.

Overcoming Objections

Occasionally an attorney will say "No" with an objection—that is, a reason not to use you other than he or she doesn't need your services right now. Part of marketing your services as an LNC is learning how to overcome these objections so your business can become successful. Here are the main objections, as well as ways you can respond:

1. **"We do it ourselves."** This is a tough hurdle to overcome. You say, "I understand. Could you make a referral for me to someone who *could* use my services?" If the attorney agrees to make the referral, then you contact Attorney B and say that Attorney A referred you. Because of the first attorney's referral, you have instant credibility and are more likely to get somewhere with Attorney B.

2. **"We'd rather hire a doctor."** You say, "My services are a lot less expensive than hiring a doctor. Wouldn't you rather find out at a lower cost if your case has merit?"

3. **"We have an in-house legal nurse consultant."** You say, "That's great. I am glad you value the services of an LNC. I wonder if I know them. What is your LNC's name?" Then you become friends with that LNC. There's always the chance that person will need to take

maternity leave or a long vacation or be too overloaded to handle everything. You're waiting in the wings, ready as a fill-in.

4. **"We don't get paid until we have a successful case" (from attorneys for a plaintiff).** You say, "My services can be expensed as an expert fee to the client. If the case is successful, you'll get the money back." To defense attorneys, you say, "My services can be expensed as an expert fee to your client. Wouldn't your insurance carrier pay for my expertise?"

As this latter example points out, LNC work is an expense of case preparation. You are a behind-the-scenes consultant. You are not part of the contingency fee the lawyer charges the client—the percentage the attorney will take of a monetary judgment for the client if he or she wins a case.

That's important for two reasons. First, you avoid any suggestion you are a hired gun who will say anything in a report to help the attorney win a monetary judgment. It is also improper in many states to share a contingency fee with non attorneys. Second, and most important, you get paid no matter whether the attorney wins or loses.

So be ready when an attorney raises an objection to using your services. **Being prepared for the objections is the most important part.** If you are not prepared, you will look like a deer in headlights. Your responses should be based on the value you bring so they will understand the benefits of your services and want to use you.

Exercise: *What objections have you heard in your marketing efforts? How do you bring value to overcome the objections?*
Objections:

_____

_____

_____

_____

_____

How I bring value to overcome those objections:

_____

_____

_____

_____

_____

_____

_____

_____

_____

_____

_____

Notes

_____

_____

_____

_____

_____

_____

_____

_____

_____

_____

_____

_____

_____

_____

Notes

Chapter Four:
Where to Look for Clients

Think outside the box. New LCNs often struggle with getting past the gatekeeper. Gatekeepers, i.e., secretaries and receptionists (or as I affectionately call them "Dobermans," as their job is to protect the attorney), are more likely to pass you through to the attorney if you have the name of a mutual friend or client.

To use this technique, start by making a contact list or a potential client list. Ask everyone you know "Who's your attorney?" or "What attorneys do you know?"

When you reach the attorney's gatekeeper, you can then honestly say, "Jane Smith referred me. He represented her in a personal injury case." You're more likely to get through to the attorney than if you simply said, "May I talk with Attorney X? I'm a legal nurse consultant."

Listen for these clues in conversation as well. If somebody says to you, "Well, Attorney A did my divorce," you can then call Attorney A and say, "So and so sent me. I know you do divorce work, but who do you refer your medical malpractice cases to?" Or "To whom do you refer your personal injury cases?" And then when you call Attorney B and mention Attorney A referred you, again Attorney B is more likely to take your call. You now have an intro and you can give them your elevator drill.

Think outside of the box. Most nurses target medical malpractice attorneys but other attorneys deal with medical information. Try personal injury attorneys, social security disability attorneys, workers compensation attorneys and even criminal attorneys. Also, don't limit yourself to attorneys. Try risk managers at hospitals, claims adjusters at insurance companies, the list can go on and on. Be creative because business is everywhere. All you have to do is ask for it.

Another great way to market your services is to be an expert witness. An attorney must have an expert to prove his case in Court. An attorney does not have to have an LNC. If you work for an attorney as an expert and do a good job, you will have instant credibility to ask the attorney to allow you to consult on other cases. This is a great way to get your foot in the door. Be careful when you work as an expert, not to advertise your work as an LNC.

Niche or Not?

When you start out as an LNC, you will likely take any case you can find. After that, some people think you must have a particular niche—say, personal injury, workers compensation, medical malpractice or product liability or even particular medical expertise like only taking OB cases.

While specialization will make it easier to market, I think when you are starting out you should stay general. For one thing, even LNCs who have niches usually have to work several niches to have a profitable business.

Admittedly you may want to choose working for the trial attorney or defense side, depending on which side gives you the most satisfaction. Here's why you want to limit yourself to one or the other: Let's say you work a case for a trial attorney representing John Doe. After that case concludes, the defendant's attorney sues John Doe. John Doe would naturally be concerned about the damage you as an LNC already familiar with his case could do in the second lawsuit if you worked both sides of the legal street.

Other than choosing trial or defense attorneys to work with, I suggest you go as broad as possible and not limit yourself to one niche or specialty. The reality is that even if you are not, say, an LNC who specializes in OBGYN cases and an OBGYN case comes to you, you know how to find the answers in that situation.

Finding Clients

You want to target the attorneys most likely to need your services. One good place to find them is in the Martindale-Hubbell Law Directory (www.martindalehubbell.com). Attorneys are listed by state, city, firm and individual attorneys. In many of the listings you can look at the "Statement of Practice" and "Firm Profile" to see what kind of work the firm does.

If listed, look at the "Representative Clients" list to see if they work with hospitals, insurance companies (on medical malpractice and personal injury cases), or corporations (product liability). These would be good attorneys for you to target. Conversely, if the list indicates the firm handles bankruptcy, intellectual property and other issues not requiring the expertise of someone like you, you know not to target them.

The American Bar Association (www.americanbar.org) is another good source of prospective clients, i.e., "prospects," with memberships divided into sections, divisions and forums devoted to different areas of legal specialization. The ABA has city, state and national chapters. As a consultant, an LNC can join as an "Associate."

Trial and defense lawyers also have their own associations—another good source of prospects. Please see the Appendix in the back of the book for links to law associations.

And don't forget Chambers of Commerce. Their events are good places to meet and mingle with attorneys.

Turning Prospects into Clients

Imagine the marketing process as a big funnel. The wide mouth of the funnel represents potential clients or prospects. These folks could benefit from your services but may not know that LNCs exist. You will need to spend time and money educating them about what you, as an LNC, can do for them. This will require multiple "touches," i.e., multiple contacts with them via meetings, phone calls, e-newsletters, etc.

Once you have educated a prospect about what an LNC does, this person moves down the funnel into a smaller group of prospects who know about LNCs but are not convinced they need one's services. They may not understand exactly what you do or worry that your services will cost more than they actually do. They may think that an LNC is a sort of expert witness and not understand the behind-the-scenes consultant aspect of your work. They may have worked with an LNC before but were not impressed by the experience.

You want to spend even more of your marketing dollars and time on this group of prospects because you want them to think of **you** when the need arises for an LNC. Your mission is to educate them about your services and what you can do in terms of solving their problems.

As you convince these folks that an LNC is a great behind-the-scenes asset, you move them farther down the funnel into a narrower, smaller group. These are the people who understand what an LNC does, have a case or other work waiting, or are actively looking for an LNC. The ideal situation is that they think of you when they need an LNC.

You spend your most marketing dollars and time here, so you can send them over the tipping point and they pick up the phone and call you. That's the point when they move from prospect to client.

Occasionally you will get a call seemingly out of the blue from an attorney you haven't targeted in your marketing. It's not luck; it's the result of all your hard work and marketing efforts. Perhaps he heard about your excellent work from another attorney. Perhaps he mentioned he needed an LNC, and another attorney who has received your marketing materials said, "Hey, I know who you should call."

My point is, you still get this call because your good work and your marketing skills earned you a referral from another attorney.

Word of mouth, i.e., a referral, is the best way to get clients. It doesn't cost any of your marketing dollars and it's relatively easy and painless. To get a referral, you simply have to maintain a good relationship with an existing client. Perhaps when you finish a case and the client is satisfied, you ask for a letter of recommendation.

Every time I have worked on a case, I follow up in two weeks to make sure the client is happy and has everything she needs. If additional work needs to be done, I pick a date with the attorney to follow up so I don't lose out on that business. If the client is happy, I ask her to write a letter of recommendation. You should get a classy, leather-bound notebook or binder and display sample work product and your letters of recommendation in page protectors. This way it looks nice, and when you're at an event people can't take this material with them.

You need to remember that marketing is a numbers game. The more attorneys you target, the more likely it is that some will have medical-related cases and need an LNC. The more contacts you make with these prospects, the more likely they will think of turning to you when a medical-related case comes along.

For an attorney to contact you, he must first have a case with medical issues and realize that he could benefit from the services of an LNC. Your marketing is critical in the next two steps—making sure the attorney thinks of you and knows how to contact you (phone and e-mail).

At times you will send out a bunch of marketing, not hear anything, and wonder if your marketing is having any effect. Consider this: Companies that do direct-mail marketing consider a 1 percent response rate a good response to a mailing. This means that if you target 100 attorneys with your marketing, one or two might respond.

Doesn't recommend

How do you keep clients once you have them? Do good work to keep your clients happy, of course. Follow up with them. Stay in regular contact.

The biggest thing is establishing a personal relationship. People want to work with people they like and consider their friends. For this reason, I am not an advocate of direct mail as you cannot create a relationship with mail.

So if a client mentions his daughter is getting married in a few months or his son is graduating or the family is taking a vacation trip to the Bahamas, make a note on the back of his business card and be sure and send a card or note or mention it when you call. "How was the Bahamas trip? What are the wedding plans coming along?" "Is your son ready to go to (college name)?" Etc.

The devil's in the details—not just the work, but also in the maintaining the personal relationships.

Do Your Homework

Marketing doesn't need to be flashy, but it should be useful to the attorney. To be useful, you need to think ahead and do your homework. Not doing your homework can cost you business and be quite embarrassing. Here's one example of a faux pas that resulted from not doing the detailed homework.

A few years ago I exhibited at the Indiana Trial Lawyers Association meeting and I wanted to offer some kind of give-a-way so the attendees would take my name home with them.

I looked at all sorts of gadgets, including those pens that are shaped like a hypodermic needle, but I thought, oh gosh, that's probably a little bit too flashy. So I settled on those magnetic business cards (you know the kind: you peel off the protective thing and stick on your business card). I thought it would be great because they'd all go home and put my business card on their file cabinets, and they'd always have it in a place so they'd remember to call me.

Well, here's the funny part: My cool magnetic business cards were demagnetizing all the attendees' credit cards. Oh, no. It was pretty embarrassing.

One of the legal nurse consultants I saw exhibiting at a different conference was giving away automobile sun visor sunglass holders with her name on them. I'm still not sure an attorney would be thinking about a legal nurse consultant in the car, but I appreciated her creativity. Again, it doesn't have to be flashy, but you want it to be something useful to the attorneys and provide value.

I've also had some good luck with other promotional items. Here's one of my best marketing ideas. It successfully showed my understanding of the attorney's problems in a promotional item and gave value.

I came up with a bookmark of medical abbreviations. At the bottom of the bookmark, it says, "If you have trouble finding any of these abbreviations, go to AcronymFinder.com or call me."

I carry them everywhere so I can start joking with an attorney when I give it to him or her: "Here's a list of medical abbreviations. So when you're looking through your medical records, you'll have a bookmark to keep your page. And then when you get frustrated at the terminology, you can call me."

The attorneys to whom I've given it love it.

Exercise: *Come up with five promotional items that would address attorneys' needs and give them value.*

1.

2.

3.

4.

5.

Notes

_____

_____

_____

_____

_____

_____

_____

_____

_____

_____

_____

_____

_____

_____

_____

Notes

Chapter Five:

Creating Effective Marketing Materials

You need crisp, professional-looking marketing materials such as a good business card and website. These show you pay attention to detail and know how to communicate—important qualities, given what attorneys need from LNCs.

Remember the old saying, "You never get a second chance to make a first impression"? Your marketing materials are that first impression. As such, you should carefully plan them and make sure you can be proud of them when you see them. They speak to your credibility as an LNC.

Business Cards

When you meet an attorney, you will give him or her your business card. Hopefully they will hang onto it and contact you when they need an LNC. Your business cards should be professional printed on a good quality card stock.

Your card should have the name of your business, your name, any certifications or degrees

("RN"), your website, email address and phone numbers.

Some tips about business cards:

- Use a simple, readable font such as serif for most of the card.
- Your name should be in a larger type size than your address.
- Make sure your email address and phone number(s) are in an easily readable font and a good size.
- Have a professional email address. Gmail is fine but nothing cutsy like fabulousnurse@____.com Be professional.
- If you offer several main services, include them as bullet points (but only if the card doesn't look cluttered). The back of the card is a good place to put this information.

While the business card is about you, all other marketing materials are about the *client*. They should emphasize the client's problems and the value and benefits your services can provide. You and your background should not be the main focus except if it impacts how you can help a client.

Websites

If you'd like to see the client-centered focus in action, take a look at the home page of my website (www.brownlaw1.com). Note the title is "Assisting Attorneys with Medical Issues in their Cases"—how I can be a resource for attorneys.

Then the copy says: "Brown Law Office was created to serve attorneys by providing advice and consultation to them on medical issues in their cases. Brown Law Office provides attorneys with an extra hand to meet deadlines and move cases to early resolution without the necessity of a salary commitment due to fluctuations in workload, benefits, or overhead."

In other words, I can help attorneys address medical issues in their cases and financially it's more reasonable to use me as a consultant than pay a salary, benefits or overhead for an in-house person.

The copy is all about how the attorneys benefit. It's about them, not me.

My website also shows you don't have to spend a ton of money for a website to be effective. I have the home page, an "About Us" page that explains my background and credentials, the legal services I provide, an "In the News" section where attorneys can learn from cases I've participated in or followed, and most importantly "Contact Us" with an email form. You could just as easily have your phone number(s) and email address there.

That's about all you need from your website. Rather than spending a gob of money having a website developer put this together, particularly when you're starting out, I suggest using something like Wordpress.com. There you'll find templates that you can plug your copy and any photos into fairly easily.

I can't emphasize enough that your marketing materials don't need to be fancy. Keep it plain and simple. Talk about the client's problems and how you can solve them. Some LNCs pour money into expensive brochures and folders; more often than not, they'll wind up unread in some attorney's trashcan.

Instead, use your *website* as your brochure. It's a lot cheaper than printing up a bunch of brochures that you're going to stress out about and worry if anyone ever reads them.

Effective marketing can be as simple as a little video on your website in which you explain who you are, what you do and how that can benefit attorneys.

On my website a 47-second video talks about how attorneys can avoid taking a case without merit by using my services. In the video I explain I prescreen cases with medical issues for merit, perform relevant research, and provide the attorney with an expert so the attorney is on top of everything in the case. Note the client emphasis again.

The video adds a nice personal touch to the website, and today with webcams and digital cameras these are very easy to shoot and add to your website.

The video ends with a plug to sign up for my newsletter about "hot topics in medicine." That newsletter provides valuable, useful information to attorneys and keeps my name in front of them. In addition, when they sign up, I receive their email addresses and can begin marketing to them.

I'll have more on newsletters as a marketing tool in a subsequent chapter. For now, try writing the copy of the home page of your website.

Exercise: *Create the copy for the home page of your website. First, write a few lines, no more than two or three sentences, explaining how an attorney can benefit by using your services:*

_____

_____

_____

_____

_____

_____

_____

_____

_____

Next, look at what you have written and write a short headline (title) that captures how an attorney can benefit from using your services.

_____

That's your home page. You will also want to include a photo of yourself; people like to see who they will be working with.

*Now write an About Us page that explains your background and credentials **as they apply to helping an attorney solve problems in cases with medical issues.***

_____

_____

_____

_____

_____

_____

_____

_____

_____

_____

_____

_____

_____

_____

_____

_____

Once you add a Contact Us page, and perhaps one with samples of your work, you have written your website.

Let's talk about samples of your work for a moment. Because of the confidentiality of a plaintiff's medical record, you should disguise the names of the patient(s), hospitals and doctors involved. Even then, I would say only use the information as a sample if the case is already settled and closed and do not chose a unique fact situation.

Whether presenting these samples to a prospect in person or showcasing samples on your website, you don't give a complete case chronology or report. I would recommend against it. Instead, show sample pages of various types of work product such as timelines, narrative pages, chronologies, etc., from different cases.

The purpose of these samples is to show that you can prepare information in different formats as preferred by different clients. The prospect will then think, "If she can work with all these attorneys with their different preferences, she can surely work with me."

Don't leave work product samples behind with potential clients. The danger is that an attorney will give your hard work to a paralegal or legal secretary and say, "This is an example of how to do our cases." Of course, this situation becomes moot when you have already done a case for an attorney and the firm knows how you work.

On Resumes and Certification

LNCs often ask me if they should include a copy of their resume in their marketing materials. I say no, don't include it unless you are seeking expert witness work. While it's OK to talk about your background in terms of establishing your expertise, I say hold off on an actual resume with dates of when and where you earned your degree(s) and places you've worked.

Why? It falls in the TMI category—Too Much Information. It can be a distraction from the information you really want the prospect to look at, namely how you can solve his problems.

If an attorney asks for your resume, then send it to him by all means. Have a well-done, professional-looking resume and keep it updated so if someone asks for it, you can send it right off. Otherwise, don't volunteer your resume until someone requests it.

The exception here, as I said, is if you want to do expert witness work as an LNC. In that case, your resume will be more extensive than a resume; it will be a *curriculum vita* (CV), which includes details on publications, talks and other work you've done that is relevant to your expertise as an expert witness. Unlike a resume, it can go on for many pages. I suggest not including your LNC work on your expert resume. This opens the door to cross examination and the jury thinking you are part of the legal team rather than a neutral medical expert giving your opinion on the case.

In terms of certification, I find LNCs worry more about this than the attorneys I've come into contact with. To be perfectly honest, nobody is going to ask if you are certified. Don't worry about it.

Notes

_____

_____

_____

_____

_____

_____

_____

_____

_____

_____

_____

Notes

Chapter Six:

A Few Marketing Dos and Don'ts

As you begin to market your consulting business, there are right ways and wrong ways to go about it. Make sure you're using the right approach.

A few marketing dos:

Make personal contact. Remember, it sometimes can take 8 to 12 contacts before an attorney becomes a client, and you want to keep yourself visible. Marketing is a little like fishing, and you always want to fish in the pond with the most fish. So surround yourself with trial lawyers or defense lawyers — the attorneys who may need what you do.

Be confident around attorneys. Don't be afraid of them; remember, you have knowledge that they can use. They need you. They want you. They're waiting for you to ask them for their business. So, don't be afraid.

Make sure to get letters of reference. When you do a case for somebody, always follow up with a request for a letter of reference.

Charge what your services are worth. Don't undersell yourself. You have valuable services to offer, and you shouldn't give them away. You might want to start with a client attorney by offering him a discount for a first case, but let him know what your full rates are up front and what discount you're giving. Then give him a time frame for the offer. If he doesn't use your services in that time, you don't need to keep extending that discount. This will give him an incentive to hire you on his case before he loses that discount.

Promote yourself through associations. It's one of the best ways to get business. For example, I attracted a good deal of business through the Indiana Trial Lawyers Association. And every state has its own association of trial lawyers and defense lawyers. (As I mentioned earlier, see the list and links to several legal associations in the Appendix.)

You may also want to be involved in associations for legal nurse consultants like the American Association of Legal Nurse Consultants (http://www.aalnc.org), but if you want access to attorneys, promote yourself through associations for attorneys. Attend these groups' events. Become a speaker at their events if possible.

Network. Effective networking involves attending events, speaking to other people and showing a genuine interest in what they do. Instead of thinking about what you will say about your business, listen carefully when they are talking. See if there is a way you can help them by suggesting a possible source of business or giving them a contact's name and phone number.

If you sincerely try to help them, they will try to help your business too by sharing names of attorneys who could use your services.

The more relationships you build at networking events, the more your network of contacts and possible clients grows. This is called a "Power Circle," in which you choose the business relationships you want to pursue and others in the Power Circle with you benefit as well.

A Few Marketing DON'Ts

Don't send unsolicited brochures. Always talk to the attorney first. Those brochures are really expensive, and they often wind up in the trash. Frequently they don't even make it to the attorney's desk. Instead use your website as your brochure.

I know several legal nurse consultants who have developed flashy brochures and folders with samples of their work product. I still frequently receive them in the mail unsolicited. I asked one of them how much it cost for the brochure/ folder and mailing. It was something like $8. Now multiply that by the number of prospects, and that is an astronomical investment.

Let me let you in on a secret: Most attorneys don't open their mail, and the only things that get to an attorney are case-related materials. I suggest only mailing to attorneys after you have their permission so it will not go in the trash. Also provide something of value. A brochure or folder with samples of your work may not be of value to the attorney and, if they do not know you or don't need your services, it will be thrown away.

Be careful of laws regarding unsolicited e-mails. If you're just going to start e-mailing attorneys rather than calling or sending them a letter, beware so they consider them a solicitation.

Don't price yourself too high or too low. The right price is what the market will bear. Do your homework. Know what the going rate is. To know this, you might ask attorneys you know what rates they are paying or check other legal nurse consultants' websites. But find out what other legal nurse consultants charge.

Don't rely only on a website ad or directory. Develop a multi-faceted approach to getting your name out there and becoming known in the community. Get your name out there in an assortment of ways, so that you have name recognition and a positive feeling about you. This will help ensure that when an attorney has the need, he's going to call you.

Here are five different methods of getting yourself name recognition: speaking, newsletters, advertising, exhibiting and publishing. Let's look at each.

Speaking: Speaking at attorney organizations literally puts you and your business in front of your target audience. Some states mandate continuing legal education for attorneys, and several organizations provide continuing legal education for attorneys. These include state bar associations as well as law associations for trial and defense lawyers on the local, state and national levels. (See appendix for links to these organizations)

For example, the American Association for Justice (http://www.justice.org), formerly known as the Association of Trial Lawyers of America, provides resources for plaintiff trial lawyers on the national level. In addition, each state usually has a trial lawyer association; even some counties do.

To get a speaking engagement, you send a letter of interest offering to speak on topics of value to the attorneys in that association. Your letter should mention several possible topics, such as how an attorney can make sure he or she has all the medical records for a case. Generally, any medical liability issue will be a hot topic of interest to attorneys.

In addition to lawyer groups, private organizations such as the National Business Institute (http://www.nbi-sems.com/), Lorman Education Services (http://www.lorman.com/) and Foxmoor Continuing Education (http://www.foxmoor-ce.com/) , often provide continuing education seminars for legal professionals. I encourage you to attend some of these, for in addition to learning about the latest legal developments they're a good way to get business.

Here's a trick I use at seminars. I ask the seminar chair if I can do a case for them for free in exchange for a mention of my services at the program. (Yes, for free and this is the only time I give my services away!) When the chair acknowledges you at the seminar, people will come up to you afterward and ask questions. You exchange business cards, and *voila!* You've got prospective clients.

Exercise: *Write down three topics you could speak about.*

1._____

_____

2._____

_____

3._____

_____

Now write down three attorney organizations in your area that you could speak to:

1._____

_____

2._____

_____

3._____

_____

Newsletters: Permission-based e-newsletters are a great way to keep in touch with clients and prospects. Remember, you have to touch someone five to eight times before he or she becomes comfortable using your services. Your newsletter should be about current hot topics which provide value to the attorneys. The articles (and newsletter) can be short, but they must provide valuable information. (I sound like a broken record but the key to all of marketing is to show your value!)

Collect e-mail addresses from your clients and prospects and say, "I have an e-newsletter that covers some of the topics you and I have talked about. May I send it to you?" It's important to get their permission, because a) they'll be annoyed by regular unsolicited emails from you b) they won't open the email and c) sending emails to people without their permission violates SPAM laws.

Once you have an email list, it's easy to design and send an attractive, informative e-newsletter through such services as Constant Contact (http://www.constantcontact.com), Aweber (https://www.aweber.com) and Mail Chimp (http://mailchimp.com/). All of these services have free trial offers and if your list is below a certain quantity it may still be free, all offer you diagnostic tools such as tracking how many people open the e-mail. It must be possible for people to unsubscribe from your email list if they wish.

Exercise: *Jot down notes for your first e-newsletter article and what value are you providing to the attorney by having this article in your e-newsletter:*

_____

_____

_____

_____

_____

_____

_____

_____

_____

_____

_____

_____

_____

_____

Now look at the web sites for the e-mail campaign providers mentioned above. Which best suits your marketing needs: _____

Now set a date to mail out your first e-newsletter:

_____

Advertising: Advertising is expense because it requires repeated exposure. To be effective, you need to run an ad numerous times to build name recognition with your prospects. If you are interested in advertising, look at state bar association journals and publications for trial and defense lawyers. But remember: Ads alone cannot establish a relationship with an attorney and do not provide value to the attorney.

Sometimes I do run ads to remind attorneys I'm still out here. But I'll just point out that when I ask how an attorney found me (you should always ask this, to know what marketing is working for you), I've never had one mention an ad. Not one.

Exercise: *Choose an attorney publication that might be a good fit for you to place an ad. Find out the publication's ad rates:*

_____

Exhibiting: Like advertising, exhibiting is expensive, but it's a good way to get known and to build your email list for your e-newsletter. Remember I said it takes five to eight touches to have the attorney trust you and use your services. Exhibiting provides an opportunity for multiple touches.

If you choose to exhibit, you need to do a few things ahead of time. First, get a list of the attendees ahead of time and send them a postcard telling them you're going to be there. Mention that you're going to have a drawing for a prize. This is to get them to come by your exhibit and talk to you.

When I say "a prize," I'm not talking about an iPad or a GPS system. You want a prize that will be valuable to the attorneys and is connected to what you do, like a medical book or software. The prize doesn't have to be expensive. One year I gave away software for the A.D.A.M. anatomy program. That went well. They all wanted to see that program in action and try to win one. I had my laptop there and was able to demonstrate the program as well as my knowledge of anatomy.

In addition to the list of attendees, the postcard and the prize, you also want to find out in advance if other legal nurse consultants will be exhibiting at the event. Then you have to decide if you want an exclusive at the event. If you don't, you can share ideas, marketing and camaraderie with the other LNCs. Collaboration is far more effective than competition. One way to reduce costs is to share a booth with another LNC, maybe one who works in a different area.

Generally, you don't want to get into a situation where there are five or six other LNCs at a seminar; it's not worth your while. You will want to make sure your booth is located in a high-traffic area, the door or food.

Your booth does not need to be fancy. A trial is like show and tell, so the more medical products, models or illustrations you can show in your booth, the better. Attorneys will be drawn to your booth. Most attorneys have never seen a foley catheter or an IV angiocath.

If you exhibit, you should consider sponsoring a breakout session. Often the event organizers will recognize the sponsors; this is your chance to speak and introduce yourself and your program. You should also put an ad in the front or back of any materials such as a binder given to participants.

At the seminar, make sure you have a way to capture their contact information and email address. Having a door prize where they can deposit their business card into a fish bowl works. After you speak to an attorney, jot down a couple of notes on the back of his card for follow up. Be sure to add the personal things like the daughter getting ready to leave for college or getting married in a couple of weeks. When you remember the personal things about someone and follow up with a letter, it helps solidify the relationship and creates trust.

After the event, make sure you send thank-you letters for visiting your booth and speaking with you. Remind them about your services and let them know you will be calling in a few days to follow up.

As you can see just by exhibiting, you have made four touches: the postcard, at the event, a follow-up letter and a follow-up call.

Exercise: *Pick two events that would be good for you to exhibit at.*

1._____

2. _____

What are a few ideas for a good prize to give away at your exhibit?

_____

_____

_____

Publishing: The benefit of publishing an article in journals for trial and defense lawyers is not that someone will read your brilliant words and call to hire your services (although that'd be nice). The real benefit is about credibility.

When you meet an attorney and find out the kind of cases you could help him with, you can say, "Here's my article about so-and-so topic in whatever journal." Or: "I think this article will be helpful to you." It gives you instant credibility and establishes you as an expert.

Before writing an article, be sure to first either call the journal or visit their website and find out their guidelines for article topics and submissions. If you want your article published, it is imperative that the guidelines be followed.

Exercise: *Investigate three journals you could write an article for.*

1._____

2._____

3._____

Now, what are three possible article topics that would be of value for an attorney who reads those publications:

1._____

2._____

3._____

Please "do" get started on your marketing efforts. It's the only way you can build your legal nurse consulting business.

Notes

_____

_____

_____

_____

Notes

Chapter Seven:

Fees, Contracts and Billing

The most frequently asked question from LNCs is "How much should I bill?" In order to determine how much an LNC should bill for their services, one has to understand how the attorney bills.

Attorney Billing

Plaintiff's attorneys take cases on a contingency fee, which means they do not get paid unless the case settles or they win at trial. Consequently, some plaintiff's attorneys have a problem with cash flow, and it may be difficult to justify the expense of hiring a legal nurse consultant. Sometimes, plaintiffs (not the attorney) will pay their own expenses and will pay the cost of a legal nurse consultant.

Another thing to remind the Plaintiff's attorney is that the legal nurse consultant's fee can be expensed to the client, if there is a settlement. Therefore the attorney has nothing to lose but to try the LNC's services.

Defense attorneys get paid by the insurance company. There is a lot of competition among defense attorneys for insurance companies to hire them. Consequently, they reduce their rates to appear more competitive to the insurance company.

One way for the LNC to obtain defense business is to have the attorney negotiate a special rate for the LNC rather than the paralegal rate. The attorney should bill the insurance company at a higher rate for LNC services than a paralegal.

In-House vs. Independent

The next question many LNCs ask is: "Should I go in- house or be independent?" There are pros and cons to being an in-house LNC versus an independent LNC.

An in-house LNC will make less money but will have benefits, security and a consistent cash flow. Independent Legal Nurse Consultants will be able to make more money and have more flexibility over their working hours, but it may be difficult to obtain benefits and it does take a while to build a practice.

Setting Fees

If the LNC decides to go independent, how much should one bill? The not-so-simple answer is "whatever the market will bear."

LNCs should see what others charge in their area so that their rate can be competitive. Be careful not to undercut the competition because it only hurts the LNC.

Attorneys will pay more if they trust the LNC, if they have been referred by another attorney, or if the LNC has delivered an excellent work product in the past. It is not advisable to give services away in an effort to attract business. Producing an excellent work product is the best approach.

Accepting a Case

When the LNC accepts a case, she should discuss caps and deadlines with the attorney. It is important for the LNC to take into consideration the attorney's budget in reviewing this case so the attorney does not get surprised by a bill.

The cap should be the most the attorney wants to spend on the case. Coming in under the cap is always a bonus to the attorney.

Also, deadlines are important so that the attorney gets the work when they want it or need it. If there is a rush deadline, the LNC may want to consider a rush fee.

It is advisable for the LNC to put what they are going to do for the attorney and their fee agreement either in a letter or a contract so that both the LNC and the attorney have a mutual understanding of what will be done and what it will cost. The contract or letter should spell out what is included in the fee and if there is a separate fee for expenses or travel time.

The LNC should also advise the attorney if they require a retainer or if there is a minimum fee to review a case. If a retainer (prepay) is required, the attorney should also be advised that if the retainer will not cover the cost of review, the attorney will receive an additional bill with the remainder.

Furthermore, if the LNC is going to charge interest for late payment, the attorney should be advised of that fact up front.

Billing

There are two types of billing: block billing, and detailed billing. Block billing puts everything the LNC has done for the case with the total actual amount of time. Detailed billing breaks down each segment of what is performed and the actual time expended. At the end, each segment of time is added for a total amount of time spent on the case.

If something is done at no charge, such as organizing the records or research, this should be added to the billing with a notation of no charge. Attorneys love to get freebies.

Expert Fees

Should the LNC choose to serve as an expert witness in a case, it is important that the LNC discuss her fees with the attorney prior to accepting the case. The testifying LNC also needs a contract or letter which specifies any retainers (prepayment required) and if additional fees will be incurred after the retainer.

Some LNC's require the retainer to be replenished when it is depleted with another retainer. Others continue to bill on an hourly basis and expect payment with the bill.

The attorney should be responsible for travel and expenses. It is also prudent for the LNC to ask the attorney to pay for her ticket up front rather than seeking reimbursement later because the trial may be cancelled or settled and the LNC will not be out that expense, futilely waiting for reimbursement.

It is advisable not to schedule a deposition or trial without a retainer.

The LNC may also want to include a cancellation policy which states that if a deposition or trial is canceled within so many days, then there will be no refund of the retainer or you may want to only refund a portion of the retainer. The LNC should also make it clear that it is the hiring attorney's responsibility to pay for deposition time and to seek reimbursement from opposing counsel if it is opposing counsel's responsibility to pay.

The most important thing is clear communication between the LNC and the attorney so each knows what to expect of the other. This will go a long way to avoid any questions regarding the bill and making sure that the LNC is paid in the timely manner.

Notes

_____

_____

_____

_____

_____

Chapter Eight:

Productivity

Productivity absolutely affects your success. Many legal nurse consultants work from home. It is so easy to get distracted by a dirty house, a run to the grocery store, picking up the dry cleaning or going to the bank. When the buzzer for the washing machine goes off, many of us feel compelled to move it to the dryer immediately.

All of these activities rob us from our focus and prevent us from being in vision. If your vision is to have a successful legal nurse consulting practice, then productivity and focus is of the utmost importance.

The bigger vision always wins.

If your vision is to have a successful consulting practice and you are consistently running errands, doing laundry or other non-moneymaking activities

("NMMA"), you may want to change your focus and only perform moneymaking activities ("MMA") during working hours. By controlling your working hours and what you do during those hours will help you become much more productive, giving you enough time to perform marketing as well as getting the work done.

Marketing must be a primary focus. The minute you stop marketing, the minute you have no more cases coming in the door. It is easy to hide behind a computer working on a website, developing brochures and other things that are not essential to going out and meeting attorneys and getting clients.

Remember, this is a relationship business. The Attorney must know, like and trust you before he/she gives you their client's confidential medical records. Attorneys are not going to go looking for a legal nurse consultant on the internet primarily because many attorneys do not know legal nurse consultants exist and, more importantly, attorneys need to know, like and trust you before they will hire you. Would you find a doctor to remove your gall bladder from the internet? Sitting behind a computer, working on brochures, working on a website, does not create a relationship with the attorney in which they will know, like and trust you and want to hire you.

To increase your productivity, I suggest that you have a schedule with times for all your activities during the working hours. Of upmost importance is scheduling times for marketing. I suggest that you use different colors to color code the moneymaking activities that you would do during the working day.

I used to allow my moods to dictate which activities I would focus on. However, since I started scheduling what activities I want to get done, I am much more productive. I suggest color coding your activities such as **red** for research, **green** for reviewing cases, **blue** for billing and **purple** for marketing. The more specific you schedule your time, putting in your calendar exactly which marketing activities that you will focus on, you will be more productive and get things done.

I am frequently asked, "How long should it take me to review a case?" There is an old proverb that says: "The amount of time it takes to do something is the amount of time you give it." Do you ever notice when you are in a rush and you have to leave by a certain time, you are able to fly through and clean the house and have it look good? The same principles apply to reviewing cases.

Therefore, I suggest you schedule the time that is reasonably required to review the case and get it done during that time. Another time saver that I use is, I dictate all my reports and chronologies. I have a secretary to transcribe them. My hourly rate is higher than a secretary, therefore, if I am reviewing another case and making my regular hourly rate, *versus* doing typing activities, which is not a moneymaking activity, I am still ahead. I choose to focus on the moneymaking activity of reviewing cases.

In the book "Think And Grow Rich", I.V. Lee approached Andrew Carnegie to do some organizational training for his company. Andrew Carnegie felt his company was efficient and did not need any additional training. Mr. Lee asked Mr. Carnegie, "If I give you one tip to increase your efficiency, would you pay me what it is worth?" Mr. Carnegie agreed.

His tip was that, if you write down the six most important things you need to do each day, preferably the night before, and just focus on those six activities, you will be much more productive. If you cannot get one of those activities completed then it gets to be first on your list for the following day.

By sticking with a plan, the most important things, you will be much more productive. Mr. Carnegie sent Mr. Lee a check for $25,000 with a note stating that his advice was invaluable and that the $25,000 does not even compare to what that was worth.

Remember, this book was written in the 1950s, therefore $25,000 back then was a huge amount of money. So, I would give you the same advice as Mr. Lee and write down each of the six most important things that you want to accomplish each day.

When I first started doing this I would write down: redo website or write book. I would have some big goals. My advice to you is to break it down in small pieces such as, rewrite homepage, rewrite about page. Take as little steps at a time rather than trying to do whole project at once or to write two pages of book.

Another tip to help with productivity is to find an accountability buddy. You declare to your buddy what you want to accomplish that day and then check in the following day and tell them what you completed and what you will complete this new day.

Remember, the more productive you are, the more successful you will be.

Chapter Nine:

Declare Yourself

Consider how serious you are about your marketing and how serious you are about your business. You must market to build your legal nurse consulting business. Marketing must be ongoing; the minute you stop marketing is the minute cases stop coming in the door. It's the minute your prospects and clients start forgetting that you're out there, providing a valuable service.

You must have a commitment and devotion to marketing for your business to survive and thrive. If you are passionate about what you do, you need to be passionate about letting people know what you do. If you're not passionate about marketing, you're probably not going to do it. And then your business will start having trouble.

Don't let that happen. Here's how you can develop and implement a successful marketing plan, even if marketing feels alien to you at the moment.

First, look at all of the marketing tools explained in previous chapters of this workbook. Draw up a list:

- o Here's the marketing I will do *today*
- o Here's the marketing I will do *this week*
- o Here's the marketing I will do *this month*
- o Here's the marketing I will do *for the next six months*

Then find someone—anybody—to whom you can declare what marketing efforts you're going to accomplish during these time frames. Then make your declaration to that person about your intended marketing efforts.

This process of speaking what you want to accomplish and having to be accountable to a person is important.

Take it a week at a time. But make your declarations. This will get you into a marketing mindset more quickly than by using the technique where you say, "Well, I'll do it tomorrow" or "I want to make 10 calls this week," and then nobody's there to follow up and ask if you really made those calls. When you are starting out, it's important to declare what you want to accomplish and have somebody hold you accountable.

Exercise: *Write down one marketing effort you will do each day and accomplish this week:*

1.Monday_____

_____

2.Tuesday_____

_____

3.Wednesday_____

_____

4.Thursday_____

_____

5. Friday_____

_____

Now write down the name and contact information of the person who will hold you accountable to accomplish these marketing efforts this week.
Name:_____

Contact info:

_____

Now call or email that person and tell them about the three marketing efforts you will accomplish this week. Set a date and time to connect again to see if you have accomplished those tasks.

Notes

_____

_____

_____

_____

_____

_____

_____

_____

_____

_____

_____

_____

_____

Closing Thoughts

Now it's put up or shut-up time. I've shown you how to market and build your legal nurse consulting business but more importantly having the mindset of success. Now it's your turn to take that advice and those strategies and get to work. Right now!

Ask yourself, "Am I really going to do whatever it takes to make this work?" If you aren't, you're just wasting your time and should consider doing something else. I think that'd be a shame.

That's because I know you have something special, something incredibly valuable, to offer. I know you have success within you. I know you want the freedom over your time and work environment. Put the ideas from this book into building *your* legal nurse consulting business, and go out and conquer the world!

About the Author

Lorie A. Brown graduated from the Indiana University School of Nursing with a BSN in 1982. She then attended the University of California at Los Angeles School of Nursing and obtained a master's degree.

Ms. Brown actively practiced nursing for twelve years in various areas such as medical-surgical nursing, gynecology, urology, neurosurgery, orthopedics, general surgery and home health care. Ms. Brown then attended the Indiana University School of Law and obtained her J.D. in 1990.

After law school, Ms. Brown was employed at the Indiana Department of Insurance, defending the interests of the Patient's Compensation Fund. For the next six years, Ms. Brown defended physicians and hospitals for medical malpractice.

Ms. Brown now focuses her practice on assisting plaintiff attorneys with medical issues in their cases. Because of her defense experience, she looks at cases with a critical eye and because of her relationship with hundreds of physicians throughout the state of Indiana, she is able to locate expert witnesses in several different specialties.

Find out more by visiting Ms. Brown's website, http://www.brownlaw1.com/.

Ms. Brown also provides one on one and group coaching of legal nurse consultants on growing their business. She takes LNCs by the hand, help them develop the mindset of success and hold them accountable for producing the results that they say they want to produce.

For more information, visit Ms. Brown's LNC coaching website, http://www.LNCMentor.com or http://www.LNCRevenueCoach.com

Appendix

Links to Legal Associations for Plaintiff Attorneys:

AAJ Directory
http://www.atlanet.org/cgi-bin/pubdir.pl

National Association of Trial Lawyer Executives
http://www.natle.org

The American Trial Lawyers Association
http://www.theatla.com/

The American Association for Justice
(formerly the American Trial Lawyer's Association:
http://www.justice.org

Southern Trial Lawyers Association, 13 States
http://www.southerntriallawyers.com/

206 MAPLE AVE
PEWEE VALLEY, KY 40056-9165
US

Order ID:

S06284

Order Date:	**Ref. ID:**	**Pay Method:**	**Ship Via:**
20210711	112-3854146-3889021	PO_xls_upload	USPS Media Mail

Product Description:

	ISBN:	**Quantity:**	**Shipmode:**
The Legal Nurse Consulting Workbook V4081606850		1	USPS Media Mail

Contains: Perfect bound book

Vervante Returns
400 N Geneva Rd STE C
Lindon, UT 84042

Lorie Brown

Massachusetts Trial Lawyers Association
http://www.massacademy.com/MA/

Michigan Trial Lawyers Association
http://www.michiganjustice.org/MI/

Minnesota Trial Lawyers Association
http://www.mnaj.org/

Mississippi Trial Lawyers Association
http://www.msaj.org/MS/

Missouri Trial Lawyers Association
http://www.matanet.org/MO/

Montana Trial Lawyers Association
http://www.monttla.com/MT/

Nebraska Trial Lawyers Association
http://www.nebraskatrial.com/NE/

Nevada Trial Lawyers Association
http://www.nevadajustice.org/

New Hampshire Association for Justice
http://www.nhaj.org/NH/

ATLA New Jersey
http://www.atlanj.org/

New Mexico Trial Lawyers Association
http://www.nmtla.org/NM/

New York State Trial Lawyers Association:
http://www.nystla.org/

North Carolina Academy of Trial Lawyers
http://www.ncatl.org/
North Dakota Trial Lawyers Association
http://www.ndaj.org/

Ohio Association for Justice
http://www.oajustice.org/OH/

Oklahoma Association for Justice
http://www.okforjustice.org/

Oregon Trial Lawyers Association
http://www.oregontriallawyers.org/

Pennsylvania Association for Justice
http://www.pajustice.org/PA/

Rhode Island Association for Justice
http://www.rijustice.org/RI/

South Carolina Association for Justice
http://www.scaj.com/SC/

South Dakota Trial Lawyers Association
http://www.sdtla.com/

Tennessee Association for Justice
http://www.tnaj.org/TN/

Texas Trial Lawyers Association
http://www.ttla.com/tx/index.cfm?event=showpage&pg=tlas

Utah Association for Justice
http://www.utahassociationforjustice.org/ut/index.cfm

Vermont Association for Justice
http://www.vermontjustice.org/VT/

Virginia Trial Lawyers Association
http://www.vtla.com

Washington State Trial Lawyers Association
http://www.wsba.org/ and
http://www.businessfinance.com/washington-state-
trial-lawyers-association.htm

West Virginia Association for Justice
http://www.wvaj.org/

Wisconsin Association for Justice
http://www.wisjustice.org/WI/

Wyoming Trial Lawyers Association
http://www.wytla.org/

Local Trial Lawyer Associations

Dallas Trial Lawyers Association
http://www.dtla.net

Houston Trial Lawyers Association
http://www.htla.org

San Antonio Trial Lawyers Association
http://www.satla.org

Trial Lawyers of Washington, D.C.
http://www.tla-dc.org/DC/

Defense Lawyers Associations:

The Association for Defense Trial Attorneys
http://www.adtalaw.com/

National Association of Criminal Defense Lawyers
http://www.nacdl.org

Tristate Defense Lawyers Association
http://www.tristatedefenselawyers.org/

Canadian Defense Lawyers Association
https://www.cdlawyers.org/html/index.aspx

The International Criminal Defense Lawyers Assoc.
http://www.aiad-icdaa.org/

Defense Lawyers State Associations:

Alabama Defense Lawyers Association
http://www.adla.org/

Alaska Criminal Defense Lawyers Association
http://www.akacdl.org

Arizona Association of Defense Counsel
http://www.azadc.org/

Arkansas Association of Defense Counsel
http://www.arkansasdefensecounsel.com/

California Defense Counsel
http://www.califdefense.net/

Association of Defense Counsel of Northern California and Nevada
http://www.adcnc.org

Association of Southern California Defense Counsel
http://www.ascdc.org

San Diego Defense Lawyers
http://www.sddl.org

Colorado Defense Lawyers Association
http://www.cobar.org

Connecticut Defense Lawyers Association
http://www.ctdefenselawyers.org/

http://connecticutdefenselawyers.org/

Florida Defense Lawyers' Association
http://www.fdla.org/

Georgia Defense Lawyers Association
http://www.gdla.org/

Idaho Association of Defense Counsel
http://www.idahodefense.org/

Illinois Association of Defense Counsel
http://www.iadtc.org/

Defense Trial Counsel of Indiana
http://www.dtci.org

Iowa Defense Counsel Association
http://www.iowadefensecounsel.org

Kansas Association of Defense Counsel
http://www.kadc.org

Kentucky Defense Counsel, Inc.
http://www.kentuckydefensecounsel.com/

Louisiana Association of Defense Counsel
http://www.ladc.org

Maine: Tri-State Defense Lawyers Association
http://www.tristatedefenselawyers.org

Maryland Criminal Defense Attorneys' Association
http://www.mcdaa.org/

Massachusetts Defense Lawyers Association
http://www.massdla.org/

Michigan Defense Trial Counsel
http://www.mdtc.org

Minnesota Defense Lawyers Association
http://www.mdla.org/

Mississippi Defense Lawyers Association
http://www.msdefenselaw.org/

Missouri Association of Defense Lawyers
http://www.modllaw.com/

Montana Defense Trial Lawyers Association
http://www.mdtl.net

Nebraska Criminal Defense Lawyers Association
http://www.nebraskacriminaldefense.org/

Nevada Defense Council
http://www.adcnc.org/

New Hampshire Association of Criminal Defense
Lawyers
http://www.nhacdl.org/

New Jersey Defense Association
http://www.njdefenseassoc.com/

New Jersey – Association of Criminal Defense
Lawyers
http://www.acdlnj.org/

New Mexico Defense Lawyers Association
http://www.nmdla.org/

New Mexico Criminal Defense Lawyers Association
http://www.nmcdla.org/

New York State Defenders Association
http://www.nycdl.org/ and http://www.nysda.org/

North Carolina Association of Defense Attorneys
http://www.ncada.org/

North Dakota Defense Lawyers Association
http://www.sband.org/BarAssociations/viewAssoc.asp?ID=18

Ohio Association of Criminal Defense Lawyers
http://www.oacdl.org/

Oklahoma Association of Defense Counsel
http://www.oadc.org/

Oregon Criminal Defense Lawyers Association
http://www.ocdla.org/

Pennsylvania Defense Lawyers Association
http://www.pacdl.org/

Rhode Island Defense Counsel
http://www.defensecounselri.org/

South Carolina Criminal Defense Trial Lawyers Assoc.
http://scacdl.org/site/

South Dakota Defense Lawyers Association
http://www.sdacdl.org/

Tennessee Defense Lawyers Association
http://www.tdla.net/

Texas Criminal Defense Lawyers Association
http://www.tcdia.org/

Utah Defense Lawyers Association
http://www.udla.org/

Vermont Association of Criminal Defense Lawyers
http://www.vtacdl.com/

Virginia Association of Defense Attorneys
http://www.vada.org/

Washington Defense Lawyers Association
http://www.wdtl.org/

Washington Association of Criminal Defense Lawyers
http://www.wacdl.org/

Wisconsin Criminal Defense Lawyers Association
http://www.wacdl.com/

Wyoming Trial Lawyers Association.
http://www.wytla.org/wy/

State and Local Bar Associations

State Bar of Texas
texbar.com

Austin Bar Association
austinbar.org

Austin Young Lawyers Association
www.ayla.org

Dallas Bar Association
www.dallasbar.org

Houston Bar Association
hba.org

Houston Northwest Bar Association
hnba.org

San Antonio Bar Association
www.sanantoniobar.org

Tarrant County Bar Association
tarrantbar.org

El Paso Bar Association
www.elpasobar.com

Corpus Christi Bar Association
ccbar.com

Plano Bar Association
www.planobar.org

Amarillo Bar Association
www.amarillobar.org

Denton County Bar Association
www.dentonbar.com

Jefferson County Bar Association
www.jcba.org

Pasadena Bar Association
www.pasadenabar.org

Navarro County Bar Association   (no separate link)
Hidalgo County Bar Association
www.hidalgobar.org

Frisco Bar Association
www.friscobar.org

Rockwall County Bar Association
rockwallbarassoc.clubwizard.com

Collin County Bar Association
www.collincountybar.com

Asian American Bar Association of Houston
aabahouston.com

Fort Bend County Bar Association
fortbendbar.com

Alabama Bar Association
www.alabar.org

Alaska
www.alaskabar.org
Arizona
www.azbar.org

Arkansas
www.arkbar.com

California
calbar.ca.gov and www.calbar.org

Colorado
cobar.org

Connecticut
www.ctbar.org

Delaware

www.dsba.org

Washington, D.C.
dcbar.org

Florida
www.floridabar.org

Georgia
gabar.org

Hawaii
www.hsba.org

Idaho
 www.isb.idaho.gov

Illinois
www.isba.org

Indiana
www.inbar.org

Iowa
www.iowabar.org

Kansas
www.ksbar.org

Kentucky
kybar.org

Louisiana
www.lsba.org

Maine

www.mainebar.org

Maryland
www.msba.org

Massachusetts
www.massbar.org

Michigan
michbar.org

Minnesota
www.mnbar.org

Mississippi
www.msbar.org

Missouri
mobar.org

Montana
montanabar.org

Nebraska
www.nebar.com

Nevada
www.nvbar.org

New Hampshire
www.nhbar.org

New Jersey
www.njsba.com

New Mexico

www.nmbar.org

New York
www.nysba.org

North Carolina
www.ncbar.org

North Dakota
sband.org

Ohio
www.ohiobar.org

Oklahoma
www.okbar.org

Oregon
www.osbar.org

Pennsylvania
www.pabar.org

Rhode Island
ribar.com

South Carolina
www.scbar.org

South Dakota
www.sdbar.org

Tennessee
www.tba.org

Texas

texasbar.com

Utah
www.utahbar.org

Vermont
vtbar.org

Virginia
vba.org

Washington
www.wsba.org

West Virginia
www.wvbar.org

Wisconsin
www.wisbar.org

Wyoming
www.wyomingbar.org

Continuing Education Organizations

National Telecommunications
http://www.ntca.org/

Lorman
http://www.lorman.com

National Business Institute
http://www.NBI-sems.com

Foxmoor Continuing Education (formerly Professional Educations Symposiums Inc.)
http://www.foxmoor-ce.com

Association for Nurses in Business and Legal Nurse Consultants

National Nurses in Business Association
http://www.nnba.org

American Association of Legal Nurse Consultants
http://aalnc.org

Yahoo Groups for LNCs

http://health.groups.yahoo.com/group/LNCExchange/

a great place to share information, get help and support!